# Between Earth and Sky

**Girl Scouts of the USA**

Chair, National
Board of Directors

**Kathy Hopinkah Hannan**

Chief Executive
Officer

**Sylvia Acevedo**

Vice President,
Girl Experience

**Jennifer Allebach**

girl scouts

SENIOR DIRECTOR, PROGRAM RESOURCES:
Suzanne Harper

ART DIRECTOR: Douglas Bantz

WRITER: Laura J. Tuchman

CONTRIBUTORS: Valerie Takahama, Carol Fleishman,
Rochana Rapkins, Christine Brongniart

ILLUSTRATOR: Susan Swan

DESIGNER: Alexander Isley Inc.

MANAGER, OPERATIONS: Sharon Kaplan

MANAGER, PROGRAM DESIGN: Sarah Micklem

The women mentioned in this book are examples
of how women have used their voice in the world.
This doesn't mean that GSUSA (or you) will agree
with everything they have ever done or said.

© 2009 by Girl Scouts of the USA

First published in 2009 by Girl Scouts of the USA
420 Fifth Avenue, New York, NY 10018-2798

www.girlscouts.org

ISBN: 978-0-88441-731-6

Printed in Italy

14 15/20 19 18 17

Photograph page 93:
Jason Perlow/OffTheBroiler.com

MIX
Paper from
responsible sources
FSC® C011825
FSC
www.fsc.org

# WHAT'S INSIDE

## A Road Trip to Remember

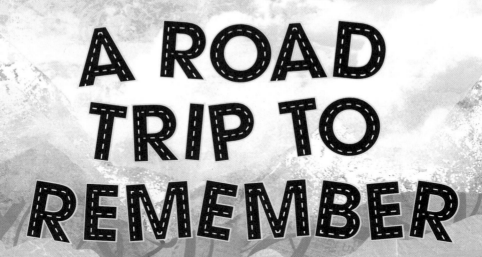

# A ROAD TRIP TO REMEMBER

**H**ave you ever traveled far, far away? So far that your suitcase traveled, too?

You might travel close to home, to a zoo or a park. Or you could just travel around the block. If it's raining, you might stay indoors. But you can still travel—from room to room or floor to floor!

So travel can be near, and travel can be far. You can even travel the world with no suitcase at all!

And that's what you're about to do. You'll travel far and wide with some pretty flower friends. They love to be outdoors between earth and sky. So turn the page. Give it a try!

# CHAPTER 1

# LUPE'S POWDER-BLUE PETAL-POWER CAR

Lupe lay flat on her back on the soft, green grass. Well, Lupe doesn't *really* have a back. She's a flower. She has lots of petals. When she lies on her petals, it's like resting on lots of little pillows.

As Lupe lay on the grass, the beautiful Daisy Flower Garden swayed and hummed all around her. Birds chirped and honeybees buzzed. Lupe paid no attention.

Was Lupe napping? No!

Was Lupe just soaking up some sun? No!

Lupe was looking under her car.

Lupe's car is light blue, just like Lupe. Powder blue, that's what she calls it. It's Lupe's powder-blue, petal-power car.

And what in the world is a petal-power car? It's a car that runs on petal power. That means flower power. Lupe and her friends make the car go. Every part of every flower helps. Help also comes from the sun and the wind and the rain. At dusk, when the sun starts to fade, help also comes from two very **bright** fireflies.

You'll meet them soon. But right now, Lupe is busy under her car. If you look under her car, you'll see lots of hoses. **And you'll smell the sweet smell** of fresh earth. If you poke your head inside the car, you'll smell that sweet smell, too.

WORDS FOR THE WISE

**BRIGHT** means full of light, like the sun. Bright also means smart. The fireflies in this story are both kinds of bright!

# FLOWER POWER

Hi, I'm Daisy. I don't look like I'm doing much. But if the sun is shining, I'm busy turning sunlight into energy.

I also "eat" through my roots. Water and food travel up my roots to my stem, and then to my leaves and petals.

Can you name all my parts?

Remember: The Daisy Flower Garden is named for me—and for all Girl Scout Daisies.

# MY *powder-blue* PETAL—POWER CAR

Hi, I'm Lupe, the lupine. I do my best to be honest and fair, just like the Girl Scout Law says. I peeled back the doors and hood of my car so you could see inside. How do you like my deep-blue bucket seats?

HEADLIGHT HAMMOCKS keep fireflies Lucy and Ace cozy.

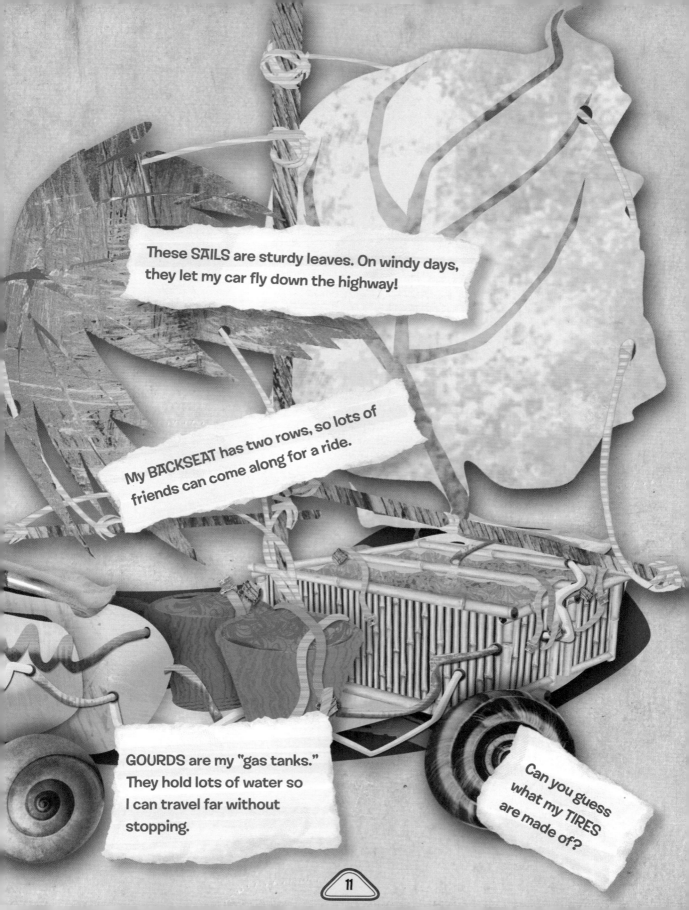

These SAILS are sturdy leaves. On windy days, they let my car fly down the highway!

My BACKSEAT has two rows, so lots of friends can come along for a ride.

GOURDS are my "gas tanks." They hold lots of water so I can travel far without stopping.

Can you guess what my TIRES are made of?

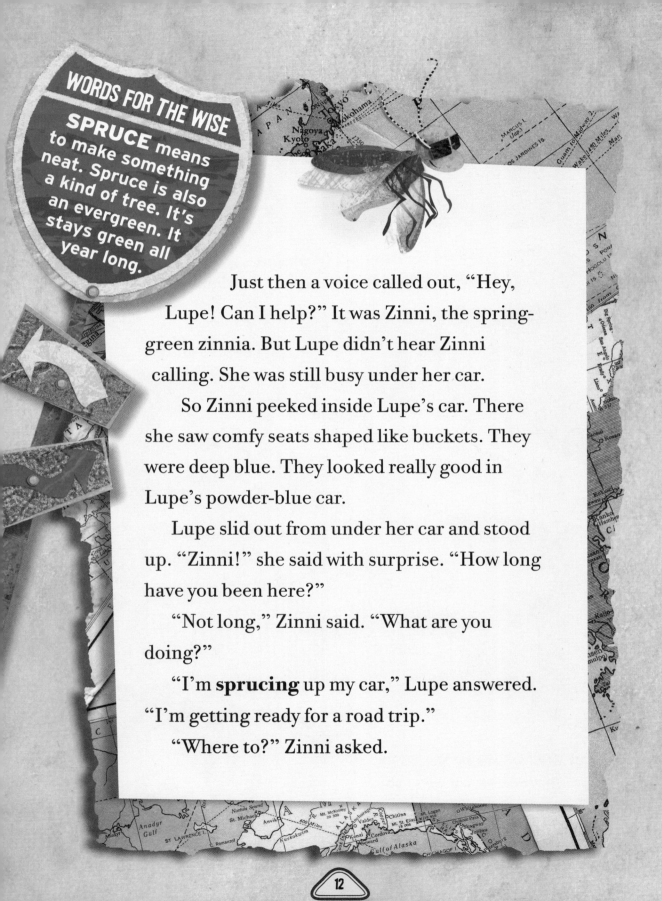

## WORDS FOR THE WISE

**SPRUCE** means to make something neat. Spruce is also a kind of tree. It's an evergreen. It stays green all year long.

Just then a voice called out, "Hey, Lupe! Can I help?" It was Zinni, the spring-green zinnia. But Lupe didn't hear Zinni calling. She was still busy under her car.

So Zinni peeked inside Lupe's car. There she saw comfy seats shaped like buckets. They were deep blue. They looked really good in Lupe's powder-blue car.

Lupe slid out from under her car and stood up. "Zinni!" she said with surprise. "How long have you been here?"

"Not long," Zinni said. "What are you doing?"

"I'm **sprucing** up my car," Lupe answered. "I'm getting ready for a road trip."

"Where to?" Zinni asked.

# Hey There, Little Firefly!

**Fireflies have many names: lightning bugs, glowflies, moon bugs, blinkies, big dippers.
In this story, the fireflies are Lucy and Ace.**

**Can you think of other good names for fireflies?**

_____

_____

"Maine," Lupe said. "That's the place to be in summer! The days are warm and the nights are cool. Why don't you join me?"

"I don't know," Zinni said. "When I'm on a road trip, the wind blows my seeds around. And my petals, too. I don't want little zinnias sprouting everywhere I go."

"Oh, Zinni, you're so **considerate**," Lupe said. "We can stop along the way and pick up your seeds and petals wherever we go."

"Then count me in!" Zinni said.

Lupe and Zinni looked out over the beautiful Daisy Flower Garden. Flowers of all shapes and colors swayed in the breeze.

"Shapes and colors," Lupe said. "That's what the world is made of! Once you know that, you can make sense of anything."

Just then, Lupe and Zinni saw their friend Clover coming toward them.

"Clover!" called Zinni. "Lupe is taking a road trip to Maine. And I'm going with her!"

"Maine! Why?" Clover asked.

# Tree Shapes, Tree Colors!

Many spruce trees grow in Maine, where Lupe is going. Most spruces are green. But some are named for a color, like the Blue Spruce you see below.

In Maine, some spruces grow on tree farms. Tree farms are places where people plant and take care of trees. Some of the trees are cut for lumber or to make paper. Some are moved to people's yards or to parks. Tree farms keep lots of trees growing on Earth.

**Blue Spruce**

What trees grow where you live? Draw them!

"For fresh ocean air, cool nights, and wild Maine blueberries," Lupe answered. "Plus, the Lupine Festival! My whole family is going."

"That sounds like fun," said Clover. "But Alaska is where I need to be. My cousin is in trouble there. At least I think she's my cousin. Her name is White Sweetclover. She's growing all over the place and kicking out all the other plants, even plants that moose eat! Why would a clover do that? And a clover with such a sweet name!"

"I have a cousin like that in California," Lupe said. "Her name is Yellow Lupine."

"Hey, come with me to Maine and then we'll drive to Alaska together," Lupe added. "We can stop in California on the way so you can meet Yellow Lupine."

"But I promised my family we'd all go together," Clover said. "Family is so important, and so are promises."

## Put Your Nose to Nature

Do you live near the ocean? Or a lake? Or a pond?
How about a forest? Or a tree? Or some flowers?

What is the air like where you live?

"My car has plenty of room for your family," Lupe said. "It has a big backseat."

You could fit a whole clover patch in here," Lupe added, pointing to the back of her petal-power car.

Clover moved to the back of the car to take a look. "Wow, this is roomy! And you have lots of seat belts," she said. "My family will be so happy. I'll go tell them to get ready for a road trip!"

And off Clover went, skipping through the grass as fast as she could without tripping over her own green leaves.

# Be Prepared!

For their road trip, the flowers pack soil and water.
What would you pack for a road trip?
What would you pack to go hiking?

**Remember: "Be Prepared"
is the Girl Scout motto!**

What to take
on my **road** trip

**What can you find in
this picture to pack
for your trip?**

**HINT: There are 23 things
to find!**

What to take on my
**hiking** trip

**Now, look at your lists.**
Do you really need all those things?
Cross out anything you can do without.

Why is it good to travel light?

## THE GIRL SCOUT PROMISE

*On my honor, I will try:*
*    To serve God and my country,*
*    To help people at all times,*
*    And to live by the Girl Scout Law.*

Clover promised to travel with her family to Alaska. What promises have you made?

_____

_____

## What promises have you kept?

_____

Draw how you feel when you've kept a promise!

# FRIENDS SHOW THEY CARE

Zinni is considerate and caring. That means she likes to help. Zinni wanted to help Lupe spruce up her petal-power car.

Being considerate and caring is one way to live the Girl Scout Law!

**When are you considerate and caring?**

_____

**How can you be considerate and caring in the great outdoors?**

_____

# CHAPTER 2

# MAINE AND THE MANY WAYS LIFE CAN BE

Just before dawn, fireflies Lucy and Ace were snug in their headlight hammocks. Their bright light let the flowers see far ahead on the road.

As the sun rose in the sky, the fireflies dozed. A golden light spread over the land.

The flowers could soon see tall, green trees, granite rock, and a sign that said, MAINE—THE WAY LIFE SHOULD BE.

MAINE
the way life should be

# Flashes in the Night

**Most fireflies sleep during the day and are awake at night. They flash their light to talk to one another.**

**How do you use light in your life?**

_____

_____

" 'The way life should be.' What does that mean?" Zinni asked. "Life isn't just one way!"

"No, it isn't," agreed Lupe. "That sign is just a way of saying Maine is special. Every place is special in its own way."

Soon the flowers reached the Morning Glory Inn. Gloria, the morning glory, ran out to greet her friends. "Lupe! Zinni! Clover! You're just in time for breakfast," she called. Platters of blueberry pancakes were balanced on her leaves.

The berries in Gloria's pancakes are wild Maine blueberries. They grow on mountains and on flat land called blueberry barrens.

**What fruits grow near your home?**

# MAINE

## FAVORITE PLACES!

Lupe likes Maine in the summertime.
Do you remember why?

_____


Name your favorite place.

_____


Do any flowers or foods grow there?

_____

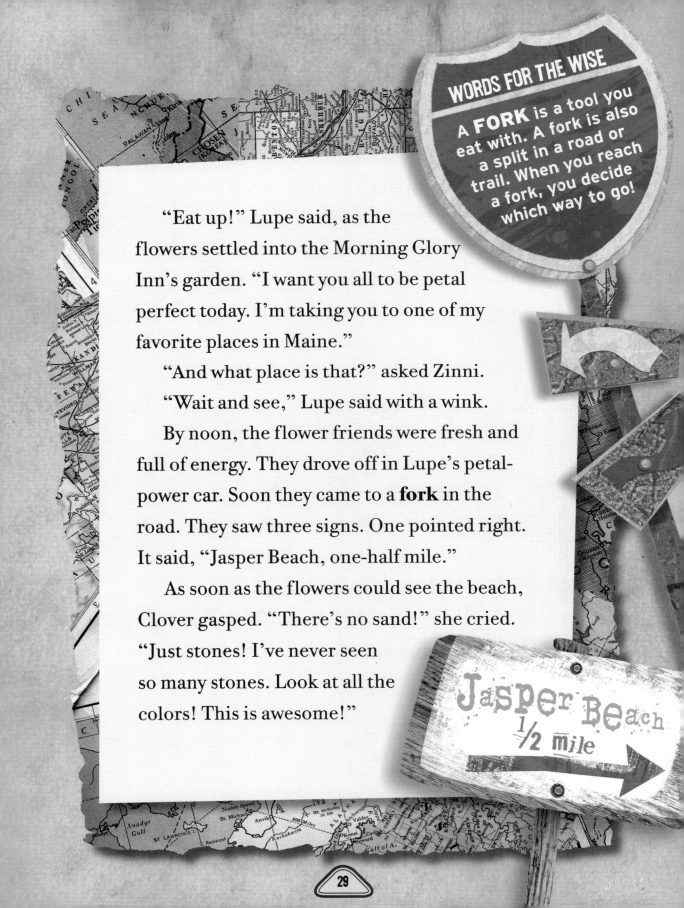

**WORDS FOR THE WISE**

A **FORK** is a tool you eat with. A fork is also a split in a road or trail. When you reach a fork, you decide which way to go!

"Eat up!" Lupe said, as the flowers settled into the Morning Glory Inn's garden. "I want you all to be petal perfect today. I'm taking you to one of my favorite places in Maine."

"And what place is that?" asked Zinni.

"Wait and see," Lupe said with a wink.

By noon, the flower friends were fresh and full of energy. They drove off in Lupe's petal-power car. Soon they came to a **fork** in the road. They saw three signs. One pointed right. It said, "Jasper Beach, one-half mile."

As soon as the flowers could see the beach, Clover gasped. "There's no sand!" she cried. "Just stones! I've never seen so many stones. Look at all the colors! This is awesome!"

Jasper Beach
1/2 mile

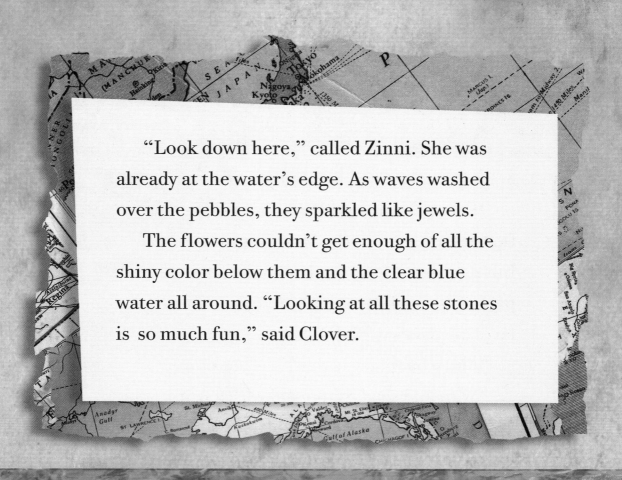

"Look down here," called Zinni. She was already at the water's edge. As waves washed over the pebbles, they sparkled like jewels.

The flowers couldn't get enough of all the shiny color below them and the clear blue water all around. "Looking at all these stones is so much fun," said Clover.

## Stone Light, Stone Bright! How Does My Stone Shine Tonight?

Find a favorite stone. What color is it?

_____

Put it in some water. How does the water change its color?

_____

"This is about as much color and shape as I've ever seen," said Zinni. "I'm going to remember this place forever!"

It was almost time for the Lupine Festival. The flowers hopped into Lupe's car and drove off to the party. When they arrived, lupines were everywhere. They were all talking at once.

"Yellow Lupine! She was so bad!" a purple lupine said. "She was such trouble!"

"Yes," agreed a pink lupine. "*People* had to come help us. I heard they pulled Yellow Lupine out of the sand dunes by hand!"

Clover turned to Lupe. "Now I'm worried about my cousin in Alaska," she said. "Is she being pulled from the ground by *people*, too?"

"That depends," said Lupe. "One garden's flower is another garden's misbehaving weed."

# MAPS + MATH

Maine's coastline is curvy and jagged. That makes it very long.

From one end to the other is longer than from the East Coast of the United States to the West Coast!

Does your state or country have any water around it? Are its borders straight or curvy? Can you find out how long they are?

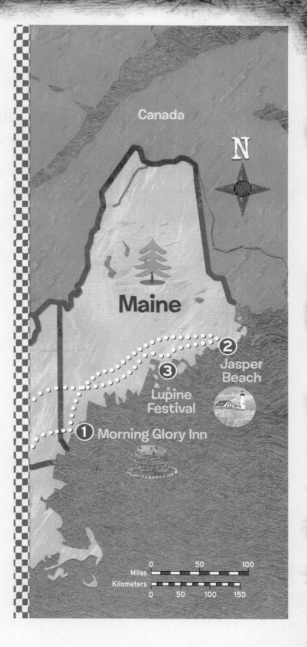

Canada

N

Maine

② Jasper Beach

③ Lupine Festival

① Morning Glory Inn

Miles
0    50    100

Kilometers
0    50    100    150

_____

_____

# SEEDS...

Seeds are baby plants just waiting to grow. They can be blown by the wind or carried by animals or water. They can stick to clothes and shoes, too. These are the ways seeds travel far from home.

How many seeds do you see floating here?
What seeds do you see where you live?
Are any of them from far away?
Ask and explore! Share what you learn!

Oh, no!
My seeds!
Stop the car!

After being outdoors, check your clothes and shoes for seeds. Don't carry seeds away from their home to yours!

# ...AND WEEDS

Weeds are plants that grow where they're not wanted.

Weeds can be beautiful. But they can crowd out important plants.

The best-known weed is the dandelion. It belongs to the daisy family, the largest flower family in the world.

Where have you seen dandelions?

_____

Have you ever blown or kicked dandelion seeds? Where did they land?

_____

# Clearing Plants and Saving Salamanders

**Sohini Bandy** lives in Austin, Texas. A big stream there called Spicewood Tributary had too many vinca plants growing by it. The vinca plants were low, like a mat, so they couldn't stop city pollution from flowing into the stream. This made the stream an unhappy place for the salamanders to live.

Sohini made a booklet to teach people about the problem and how to help. Thirty-four people, including girls who live near the stream, pulled out the vinca. Then they put in taller plants that would keep the pollution out and create a better home for the salamanders. Some of the plants had fun names like beautyberry; eastern gama grass, and obedient plant.

Sohini called her project the Clean Creek Challenge. It earned her a Girl Scout Gold Award.

Where do you see plants growing where they shouldn't? Draw them!

# The Art of Tossing Seeds

**Kathryn Miller** grew up in Brazil, by a beach.

"We had chickens and rabbits," says Kathryn, who was a Girl Scout. But slowly her neighborhood changed. Big buildings took the place of houses. The waters where Kathryn fished filled with gunk and plastic bags.

In college, Kathryn studied science to understand the changes around her. By then she was living in the United States. In California, she learned to make art from soil.

"I made these little black birds out of soil and I put them out on this big lawn," Kathryn says. She wanted the birds to break apart in the rain and mix into the ground.

Then she learned about the plants that grew in the area. She put their seeds inside her birds and threw the birds into empty lots. She also gave away some birds. People loved getting them.

The best thing about making seed birds, Kathryn says, "is that it gets people outside looking at stuff and finding places that need **vegetation**."

**WORDS FOR THE WISE**

**VEGETATION** means all the plants that grow in a place. Where do you see vegetation?

# CHAPTER 3

## SUNNY'S SUMMER AND THE ROAD TO DAIRYLAND

All the talk of Yellow Lupine being pulled from the dunes worried Clover. She wanted to reach her cousin in Alaska as soon as possible. So Lupe agreed to drive west right away.

As the flowers traveled into the sunset, Clover turned to Lupe. "I know you didn't want to leave Maine so soon," she said.

"That's OK, Clover," said Lupe. "Once we're in California, I'll be a very happy flower."

Just then Lucy and Ace flashed their lights. They had something to say.

"Just remember: We won't be much good out West," Lucy said.

"That's right," chimed in Ace. "We fireflies live all over the world. But not in California."

"Why is that?" Lupe asked.

"We're not sure," Lucy said. "No one really knows."

"Well, you're missing out on some nice weather," Zinni said. "In California, I can wash my petals and they dry right away. That's a real plus for a petal head like me!"

## Fireflies by Day, Fireflies by Night!

Nearly 2,000 kinds of fireflies live in the world. More than 170 kinds live in the United States. But none live west of the Rocky Mountains.

Can you find the Rockies on the map on pages 94–95?

Lucy and Ace flashed their lights in agreement.

As the flowers traveled along, the miles began to add up. A road sign soon appeared: "Pittsburgh, next exit."

"Pittsburgh!" yelled Zinni. "Isn't that where Sunny, the sunflower, is spending the summer?"

"Yes," said Clover. "She said she was 'getting the lead out.' What did she mean?"

# Nature's Cleaning Power!

Like sunflowers, scented geraniums are good at cleaning soil.

So are willow trees
and corn
and pumpkins.

Do sunflowers or other plants grow near you? Maybe they're cleaning! Ask around! Share what you learn!

## How Sunflowers Clean the Soil

Sunflowers pull lead out of the soil and into their roots. Then the lead moves up to the flower's stem and leaves. That way, the lead is above ground and out of the soil. Then the sunflower is pulled from the soil. Sometimes the sunflower's seeds, which have no lead in them, are made into fuel. That fuel can power lots of things.

"Sunny is cleaning the soil in Pittsburgh so more gardens can grow there," Lupe explained.

"Sunny is being very helpful," said Zinni.

"Yes, indeed," agreed Lupe. "Sunflowers are good at removing bad things, like lead, from soil. Did you know that Pittsburgh used to have really dirty air, too? It was so dirty that morning was as dark as night! That would have kept Lucy and Ace busy!"

The two fireflies flashed their lights. "Let's stop and say hello," Lucy said.

"Maybe Sunny will join our road trip," said Ace.

"I hope so," said Lupe. "Her leaves make such nice wind sails for my petal-power car."

And then she turned off the highway and drove into the city of Pittsburgh.

Gardens were everywhere. "How will we ever find Sunny?" Zinni asked.

"Just look up," Lupe said. "She's so tall, we can't possibly miss her. And she'll be with lots of other sunflowers."

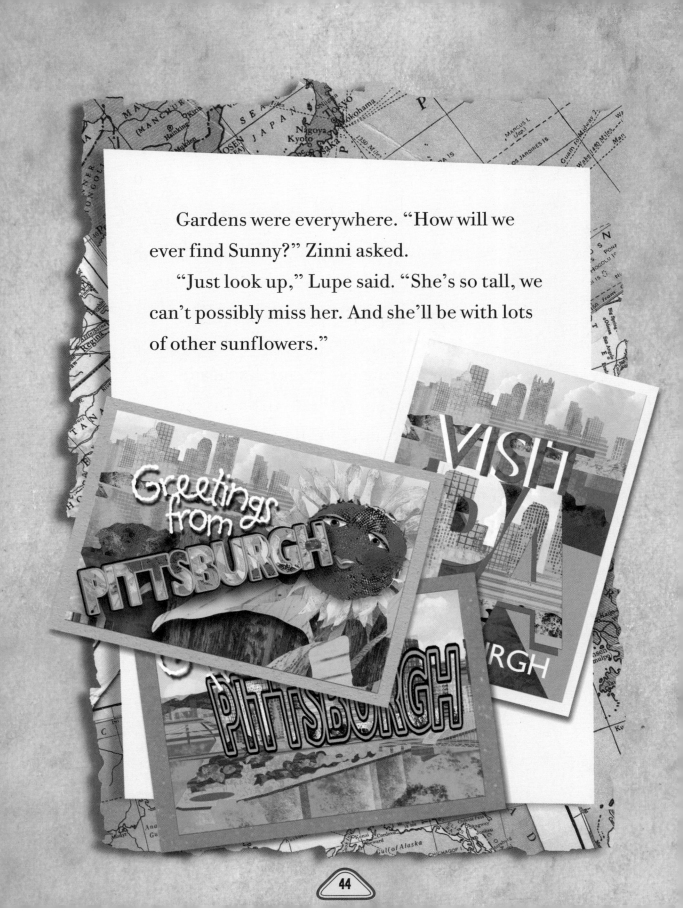

As the petal-power car turned the bend, the flowers saw an amazing sight: the city surrounded by water. They were looking at the place where two rivers—the Allegheny and the Monongahela—come together to form the mighty Ohio River.

As soon as the car turned the next bend, the flower friends saw a huge wall of sunflowers.

"Sunny!" the flowers cried all at once. "Down here! It's Lupe, Zinni, and Clover! And Lucy and Ace!"

"What a nice surprise," said Sunny, bending low to greet her friends. "I wasn't expecting any visitors."

"We're going to Alaska," Clover said.

"Alaska!" cried Sunny. "I've always wanted to go there. You know, I've been working so hard. I could use a rest. May I join you?"

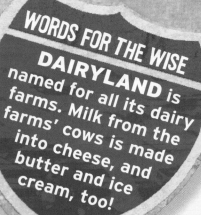
"We'd love to have you," Lupe said. "We're stopping next in Wisconsin, America's **Dairyland**. We hear the cheese is good."

"Well, then, move over!" Sunny said, as she hopped into the car and buckled her seat belt.

With strong winds and Sunny's big leaf sails, it wasn't long before the flowers reached Dairyland.

They stopped to enjoy the rolling hills dotted with farms and black-and-white cows.

"You know, these dairy farms used to be wheat fields," said Lupe. "But growing wheat season after season wore out the soil."

"Taking care of soil is so important," said Sunny. "That's why I was in Pittsburgh."

"And now that I've been in this bucket seat with its fresh soil for a while, I feel so much better," Sunny added. "How about we go taste some delicious Dairyland cheese?"

# WHEN SOONER IS BETTER!

The flower friends decide to leave Maine early so they can get to Alaska faster. Being able to change plans easily is a good skill to have.

When have you changed your plans?

_____

How did everything turn out?

CHANGE AHEAD

_____

# Pedal Power and You!

The flower friends traveled from Maine to Dairyland using their own petal power!

For the flowers, Lupe's petal-power car is an energy-smart way to travel.

Bicycles are energy-smart, too! Instead of flower power, bicycles use pedal power!

**Do you ride a bicycle? If you do, how far do you go?**

_____

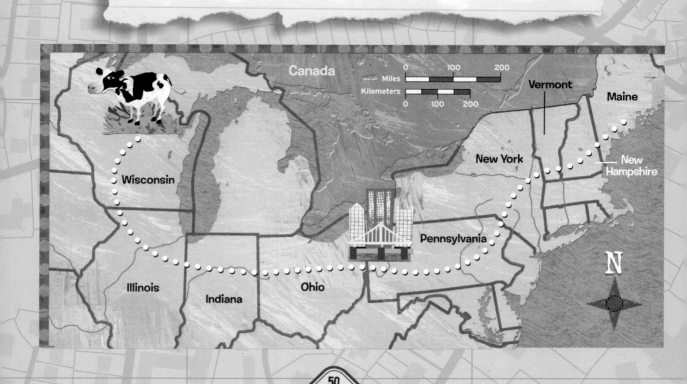

# City Farms, City Food

**Miriam Manion**'s father was a vegetable grower in Pittsburgh who was proud of his tomatoes. When Miriam grew up, she became the head of Grow Pittsburgh, a group that helps people plant gardens right in the city. This lets them enjoy fresh food close to where they live. When food doesn't have to travel far to get to those who eat it, it's better for people and the planet.

What foods **grow** near you?

# CHAPTER 4

# A SALTY LAKE AND THE SMELL OF PINE

Triangles, balls, bricks, and cubes. In Dairyland, the flowers saw cheeses of all shapes and colors—even giant wheels, all wrapped in bright red wax.

They sampled cheddar, lacy Swiss, and a cheese called Wunderbar, which means "wonderful" in German. Then, on the grass, they spread a picnic of cheddar cheese, chocolate milk, and fresh red raspberries.

"For shapes and colors, Dairyland is as much fun as Jasper Beach!" Zinni said.

Suddenly, a big, white Dairyland truck drove up. Its back door swung open and a bush with beautiful, white blossoms peeked out.

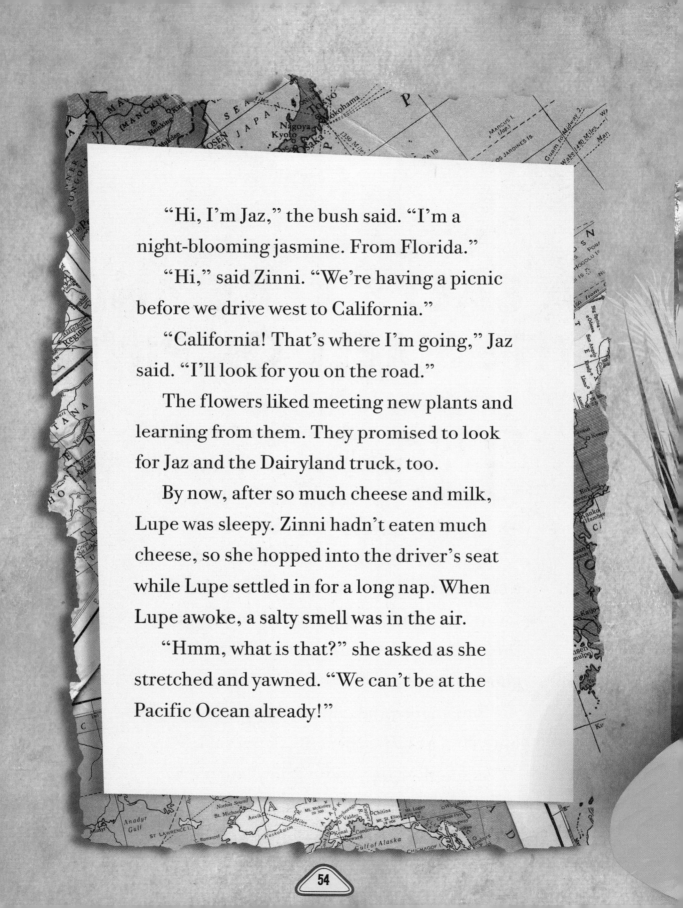

"Hi, I'm Jaz," the bush said. "I'm a night-blooming jasmine. From Florida."

"Hi," said Zinni. "We're having a picnic before we drive west to California."

"California! That's where I'm going," Jaz said. "I'll look for you on the road."

The flowers liked meeting new plants and learning from them. They promised to look for Jaz and the Dairyland truck, too.

By now, after so much cheese and milk, Lupe was sleepy. Zinni hadn't eaten much cheese, so she hopped into the driver's seat while Lupe settled in for a long nap. When Lupe awoke, a salty smell was in the air.

"Hmm, what is that?" she asked as she stretched and yawned. "We can't be at the Pacific Ocean already!"

# A GREAT LAKE FOR BIRDS!

Lots of birds rest at the Great Salt Lake in the fall, as they travel south to spend the winter in warm weather. They stop at the lake again in the spring, when they return north as the weather starts to get warmer.

What birds fly past where you live in spring and fall? What resting places for birds are near you?

_____

_____

"No, it's the Great Salt Lake," said Zinni. "It's saltier than the ocean!"

"So we're in Utah?" Lupe asked. "I was hoping we'd be in California by now!"

"I really wanted to see the Great Salt Lake," said Sunny. "Lots of sunflowers live by it. I had so much fun floating in it when I was little."

"I'm glad we're here," said Lupe. "Lots of birds like to rest by this big lake. I wonder how many we'll see."

"I hear that many ducks and geese live near the waters of the Great Salt Lake," Sunny added. "Let's see how many we can spot."

"That's a good idea," said Clover. "Lots of seagulls, pelicans, and bald eagles are also found here. Let's keep an eye out for those birds, too."

Art©Estate of Robert Smithson/Licensed by VAGA, New York, NY, Photo by Gianfranco Gorgoni

GREAT SALT LAKE

# ART IN NATURE!

Artist Robert Smithson's Spiral Jetty was built in the Great Salt Lake in 1970. The spiral is sometimes completely covered by the lake.

If you could make art outdoors, what would it look like? How would it help Planet Earth?

Draw it!

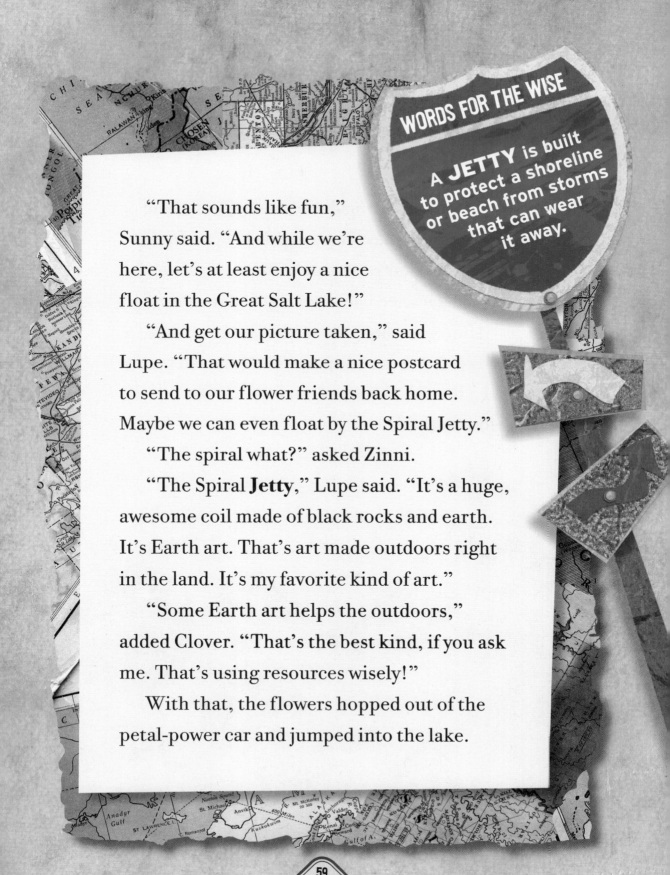

"That sounds like fun," Sunny said. "And while we're here, let's at least enjoy a nice float in the Great Salt Lake!"

"And get our picture taken," said Lupe. "That would make a nice postcard to send to our flower friends back home. Maybe we can even float by the Spiral Jetty."

"The spiral what?" asked Zinni.

"The Spiral **Jetty**," Lupe said. "It's a huge, awesome coil made of black rocks and earth. It's Earth art. That's art made outdoors right in the land. It's my favorite kind of art."

"Some Earth art helps the outdoors," added Clover. "That's the best kind, if you ask me. That's using resources wisely!"

With that, the flowers hopped out of the petal-power car and jumped into the lake.

The salt water made floating so easy. The flowers didn't have any trouble keeping their heads and their roots safely above the water. They just leaned back and enjoyed the view.

After a nice long float, the flowers were ready to hit the road again. They wanted to reach the pinewoods of northern Arizona before dark.

# The Great Salt Float!

The flower friends can float easily in the Great Salt Lake. So can people. That's because salt water is heavier than plain water. The lake's water has enough salt in it to support a person's weight. To lie back and float on the lake is a fun thing to do!

# SALT, WATER, AND YOU!

Put some warm water into a bowl and see what will float in it and what won't. Try some things that won't be hurt by the water—maybe a pebble, a pencil, and a small, bouncy ball. What floats? What sinks?

Add a tablespoon of salt to the water and mix it in well. Now see what floats and what sinks. Did you see anything new?

Add another tablespoon of salt, and mix it well. See if anything new happens. Keep adding salt until something that sank before floats. How much salt did you have to add before more things would float?

As they drove south, the flower friends smelled sweet pine sap in the air. "These aren't just any pine trees," Lupe explained as beautiful woodlands came into view. "These are piñon pines. Their seeds are pine nuts, an important food for birds and people for thousands of years."

## MAKING GOOD USE OF EVERY LITTLE THING!

Clover makes good use of everything she has. Her leaves give the Daisy Flower Garden a nice green carpet. Her sweet nectar helps honeybees make delicious clover honey. That's using resources wisely, just like the Girl Scout Law says!

# North, South, East, or West?

As the flower friends travel from Wisconsin's Dairyland to Arizona, they make three big turns.

In what direction are the flowers going before each **turn?**
When they turn, which way do they go?

# Piñon Pines, Piñon Nuts, Piñon Jays

The seeds of piñon pine trees are tasty. They're called pine nuts. People like to eat them. So do birds called piñon jays.

As jays collect and store the nuts, so they have food throughout the seasons, they also scatter the seeds. That helps new trees grow.

# Piñon Pines Make a Comeback!

**Lisa Floyd-Hanna** lives in Prescott, Arizona. She studies piñon pine trees in Mesa Verde National Park, where a beetle called Ips has been hurting the trees.

The Ips beetle, says Lisa, is dark brown, "really ugly," and "about the size of half a pinkie nail."

Ips beetles like the smell of piñon pine sap. They feed on sugars and other food under the trees' bark. When lots of beetles attack, you can hear them, Lisa says: "It's a *ch-ch-ch-ch* sound. It's like they're chewing! It's creepy."

Ips beetles carry a **fungus** that infects the piñon pines and kills them. The fungus turns the wood of the trees blue. Some people use the blue wood to make furniture. That way it doesn't go to waste!

When the beetles first attacked, the piñon pines were already weak from dry, hot weather. That's why so many of them died so quickly.

But now, new piñon pines are sprouting from piñon seeds, and Lisa is happy to see them. "It's kind of awesome," she says.

## WORDS FOR THE WISE

A **FUNGUS** can be good or bad. A bad fungus can kill trees. A good one can help make cheese!

# CHAPTER 5

# TOWARD THE COAST OF CALIFORNIA

With the pines of Arizona behind them, the flowers traveled south and west into the desert. They talked about all the piñons they had seen: piñon pines, piñon nuts, and piñon jays.

"I love the smell of pine trees," Lupe said.

"It's good that they're growing again," said Clover. "But I'm still worried about my cousin in Alaska."

"Alaska, here we come!" cried Sunny.

"First we're going west to the coast of California," Lupe reminded her friend.

"And before that, we have to cross this hot desert," Zinni added.

The flowers gazed at the flat, sandy land all around them. Brown mountains in the distance looked like bare rock. As they traveled along, spindly plants tumbled all around them. One even tumbled right into the side of the petal-power car and stuck to it.

"Hi, I'm Tatiana the tumbleweed," the plant said.

"A real live tumbleweed?" asked Clover. "Wow, we really are out west!"

"I'm not from here," said Tatiana. "Well, I grew up here, on a tumbleweed farm. But my family is from Russia. They came to America when they were just seeds. They hopped into a bag of

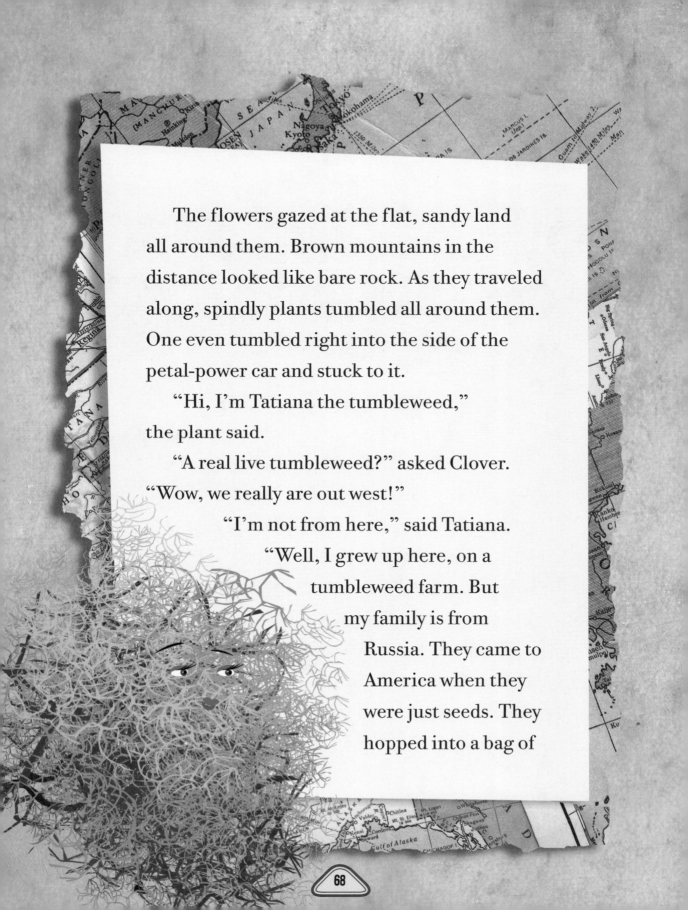

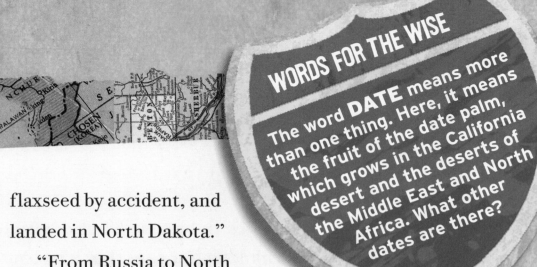

WORDS FOR THE WISE

The word **DATE** means more than one thing. Here, it means the fruit of the date palm, which grows in the California desert and the deserts of the Middle East and North Africa. What other dates are there?

flaxseed by accident, and landed in North Dakota."

"From Russia to North Dakota! That's pretty far traveling for a seed!" said Zinni. Right now, she was trying her best to hang on to her own seeds in the hot, blustery wind.

"That's nothing," said Tatiana. "We've since tumbled north to Canada and south to Mexico." Just then a gust of wind blew Tatiana off the petal-power car. She tumbled onto the road and into the desert brush.

"Bye, Tatiana," the flowers called out as their car kept moving on. Soon they were in California, driving past the tall **date** trees of a town called Indio.

"How about we stop for some date shakes?" Zinni asked.

# HOT WEATHER, HOT TEA, AND YOU!

Believe it or not, on a hot day, you can cool off by drinking hot tea. That's because the tea's heat raises your body temperature and then your body lowers its own temperature to cool itself. People who live in the desert have been drinking hot tea for thousands of years. How does a hot drink make you feel on a hot day?

"Sounds like a nice cool treat to me," said Clover. "You know, our pal Daisy likes to drink hot tea on hot days. Why is that, I wonder?"

As the flowers sipped their shakes, a big, white truck pulled in next to them. DAIRYLAND was painted on its side.

"Look!" called out Zinni. "The Dairyland truck! Let's say hi to Jaz."

"Yoo-hoo! Anybody home?" Sunny called.

Jaz peeked out the back and said hello.

A blast of cool air came out of the truck, too.

"Wow, that cool air feels so nice," Lupe said. "Can we come inside?"

"Fine by me," said Jaz. "This is a refrigerator truck full of cheese. That's why it's so cool inside. But cheese isn't much fun to travel with—it can't talk. So come on in. I could use some company besides my own sweet-smelling flowers. "

"Your flowers smell *really* good," said Clover. "We've just come from the piñon pines of Arizona. They smell good, too. They're growing again after nearly being wiped out by a fungus."

"Sounds just like the chestnut trees back home in Florida," Jaz said. "That's a good comeback story, too. Have you heard it?"

# The Chestnuts Return!

   More than 100 years ago, chestnut trees grew all along the East Coast, from Maine to Georgia. They also grew west to the Mississippi River.
   Chestnuts were important food for people and animals. And chestnut wood was used for many things. Then a fungus attacked the trees. Most of them died.
   But in Ohio, one big tree lived. That tree helped grow new trees. Those new trees now live on a chestnut-tree farm in Florida.

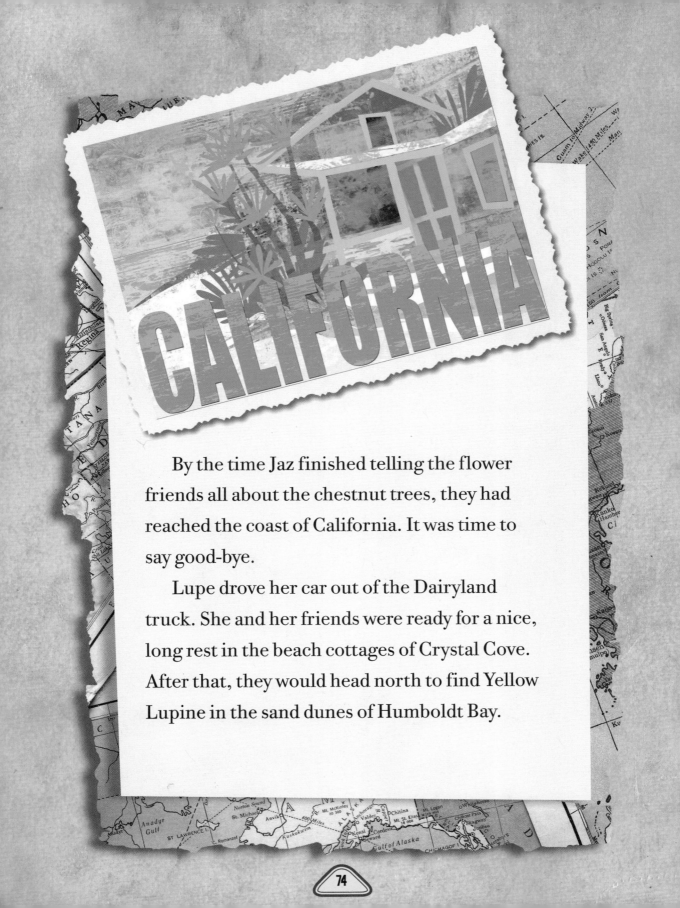

# CALIFORNIA

By the time Jaz finished telling the flower friends all about the chestnut trees, they had reached the coast of California. It was time to say good-bye.

Lupe drove her car out of the Dairyland truck. She and her friends were ready for a nice, long rest in the beach cottages of Crystal Cove. After that, they would head north to find Yellow Lupine in the sand dunes of Humboldt Bay.

# The North and South of It!

*Southern California has lots of palm trees and sunshine. Northern California has wetter, cooler weather.*

**What is the northern part of your state or country like? What is the southern part like?**

_____

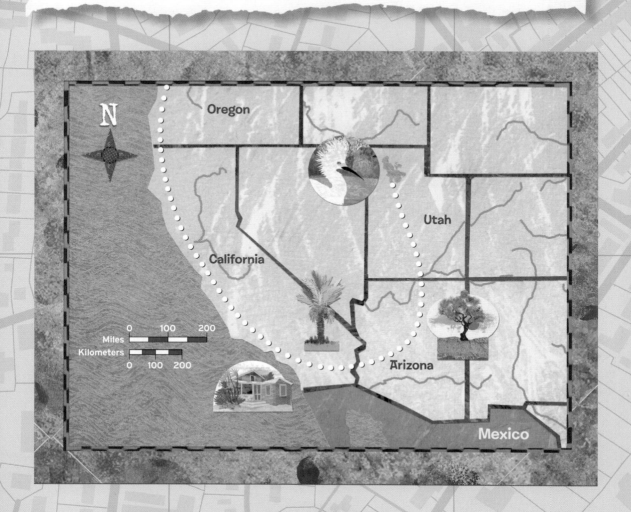

# Protecting Beautiful Places!

*Crystal Cove is a state park in California. It has a beach, woodlands, and cottages. State and national parks protect places so everyone can enjoy them.*

**What state or national parks are near you?**

_____

Dear Daisy, Mari, Gerri, and Vi,

We're in California! This is Crystal Cove. Isn't it beautiful? Wish you were here,

Lupe

......postcard......

The Flower Friends

Daisy Flower Garden

U.S.A.

# MAKE NEW FRIENDS,
## BUT KEEP THE OLD
## ONE IS SILVER
### AND THE OTHER GOLD.

When the flower friends meet Jaz,
the jasmine, they make a new friend.
But they also stay in touch with old friends.
They send them postcards of their road trip!

When have you made a new friend?

_____

How do you stay in touch with old friends?

_____

# CHAPTER 6

# NORTH TO WHITE SWEETCLOVER

From high on a sunny cliff, the flower friends looked down on the shimmering Pacific Ocean. Waves rolled in, one after another, leaving a line of white, foamy water between the sand and the sea. Up above, seagulls dipped and soared on the wind.

This was Half Moon Bay, a place as lovely as its name. "I could sit here forever," Lupe said.

"But shouldn't we get going?" asked Clover. "It's a long way to Alaska. And we want to stop to see Yellow Lupine first."

By now, Rosie the rose had joined the flower friends. She always spends the summer in California. Like Zinni, she loves the dry California air. It's good for her petals. "Fine by me," Rosie said. "The sooner we get going, the sooner we can reach Clover's cousin and make the world a better place!"

And so the flowers headed north. They passed through parklands of giant redwood trees, where clusters of ladybugs dozed in the shade. The trees' thick, reddish-brown bark was like no other tree the flowers had ever seen.

**Ladybugs on Vacation!**

Ladybugs spend the summer in the redwoods. Come fall, they gather in clusters and enjoy a sleepy vacation until the warm days of spring.

# A Giant Among Trees

Redwoods are the world's tallest trees. But their cones are small. They're the size of a grape or an olive. Each one can hold 100 seeds.

By the time they reached the sand dunes of Humboldt Bay, Yellow Lupine was nowhere to be seen. "I'm so sorry," Lupe said to Clover. "I thought Yellow Lupine would still be here. I wanted you to meet her. I guess she's back

## Why Yellow Lupine Couldn't Live Up North!

Sand dunes protect the shore from waves and give a home to wildlife. But dunes need plants to hold them in place. Otherwise the wind and the sea wash them away. In southern California, yellow lupine holds sand dunes in place. It is so helpful that people brought it to northern California to protect dunes there, too.

But in the cool, wet weather of the north, yellow lupine grew fast, and tall. It grew so tall that it blocked sunlight from reaching smaller plants. For the smaller plants to live, yellow lupine had to be pulled out.

home in southern California, where she can really help the dunes."

"On to Alaska, then!" said Sunny. "I want to see a moose!"

"Let's hurry," said Clover. "I don't want to miss White Sweetclover, too."

Traveling as far as they could by the light of day, the flowers drove north, north, north. Soon they were in Oregon, along the Columbia River Gorge. They stopped by a beautiful waterfall. "This is salmon country," said Lupe. "Millions of wild salmon once swam the rivers here. People promised to protect them forever. They need to work harder to keep that promise."

North, north, north, the flowers went. When the road became rocky and rough, they talked of taking a ferry, or even a plane.

# Keeping the Salmon Promise

The Klamath River starts in Oregon and flows south to California. Millions of salmon once swam the river. But not many swim it anymore. That's because dams were built in it. Dams provide water to farms, and they help create electricity with water power. They also block the salmon's way.

Salmon have always been important to American Indian tribes in the Northwest. They are as important as the air we breathe!

Students in the area wanted to call attention to the salmon that were gone from the river. So they ran one after another alongside the river. They called it a salmon-run relay. Three California Girl Scouts—**Rebecca Rodriguez, Molly West,** and **Tori Laurin**—ran with them. "I have grown up camping a lot and loving nature," says Rebecca. "So I just want to make sure that that's around for a long time for other girls, and for me."

"You know, Lupe," said Clover, "I've heard that you can see lots of shapes and colors from an airplane. I've heard that from the sky, the land looks just like a patchwork quilt."

"That would be fun to see someday," said Lupe. "But let's stay on the ground for now.

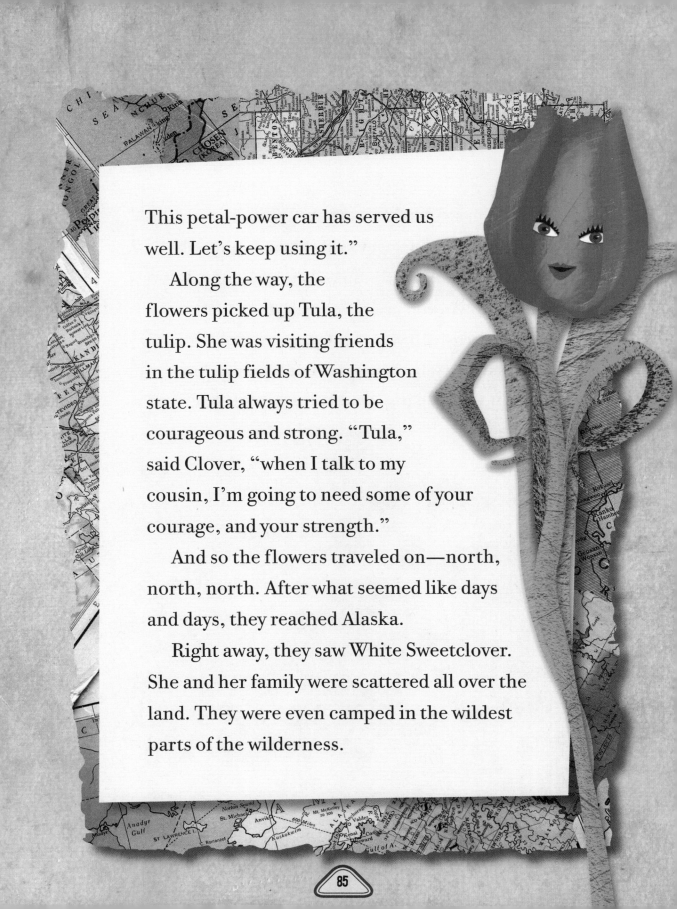

This petal-power car has served us well. Let's keep using it."

Along the way, the flowers picked up Tula, the tulip. She was visiting friends in the tulip fields of Washington state. Tula always tried to be courageous and strong. "Tula," said Clover, "when I talk to my cousin, I'm going to need some of your courage, and your strength."

And so the flowers traveled on—north, north, north. After what seemed like days and days, they reached Alaska.

Right away, they saw White Sweetclover. She and her family were scattered all over the land. They were even camped in the wildest parts of the wilderness.

"I'm so glad I found you, White Sweetclover," Clover said. "You don't look like me at all. You're so tall and scraggly. But deep down, you are my cousin, that's for sure. Underneath all your wild ways, you're really very sweet. That's why I don't like hearing about you causing trouble here in Alaska.

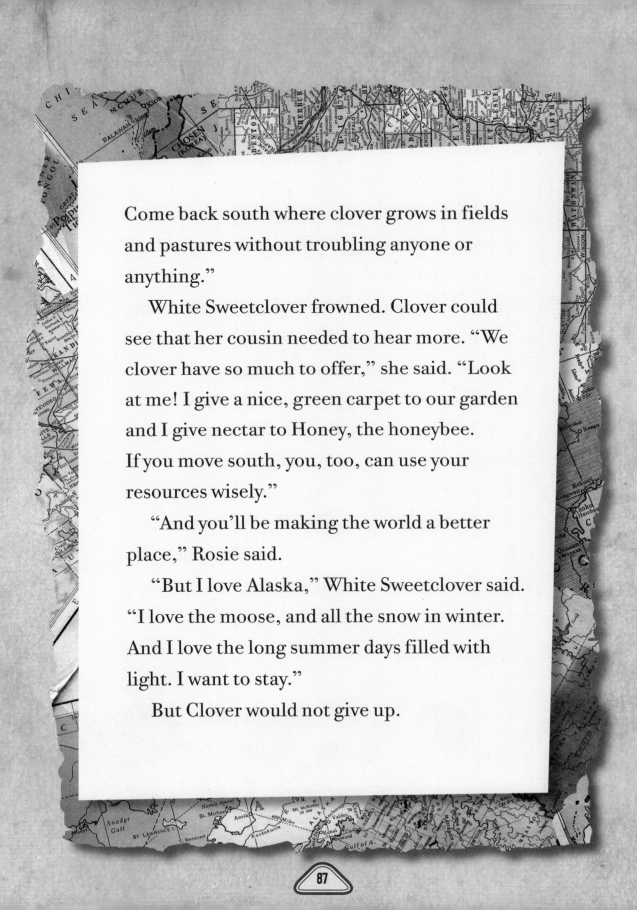

Come back south where clover grows in fields and pastures without troubling anyone or anything."

White Sweetclover frowned. Clover could see that her cousin needed to hear more. "We clover have so much to offer," she said. "Look at me! I give a nice, green carpet to our garden and I give nectar to Honey, the honeybee. If you move south, you, too, can use your resources wisely."

"And you'll be making the world a better place," Rosie said.

"But I love Alaska," White Sweetclover said. "I love the moose, and all the snow in winter. And I love the long summer days filled with light. I want to stay."

But Clover would not give up.

"You're stopping good plants from growing," she said. "Those plants are food for the moose you love!" She asked White Sweetclover to gather her family by the river to talk it over. And talk they did. They talked and talked and talked. Then they all agreed: They would move south before the first snowfall.

Clover now felt her trip to Alaska was a success. "We've learned so much about plants and seeds and where they do good and where they do harm," she said. "We know enough to help plants everywhere. Let's head home."

"But we haven't seen a moose!" Sunny said. "A photo of us with a moose would make the best postcard of all."

And so the flower friends piled back into Lupe's petal-power car and went where they love to be: outdoors between earth and sky, in the sun and fresh air, on the lookout for something new to see.

# In the River and on the Road

**Trish Wurtz** works for the U.S. Forest Service in Fairbanks, Alaska. She studies white sweetclover, the first "weed" to spread into Alaska's wilderness.

White sweetclover grows along roadsides. But it has also been found by the Stikine River. "Here's this beautiful wilderness area, far from any road," Trish says, "and because the white sweetclover seeds got into the river and flowed downstream, the clover has taken over now."

Pulling out clover by hand stops new seeds from spreading. But it can't stop seeds already in the soil. Each clover plant can make 10,000 seeds. "In some places, there are already billions of seeds in the soil," Trish says.

Trish wants white sweetclover stopped before it forces out good food plants. Moose, she explains, like to eat willows in winter. If white sweetclover pushes out willows, the moose won't have food.

## How White Sweetclover Came to Alaska

White sweetclover may have been carried north by gold miners working along the Stikine River in Canada. The clover probably fed the miners' horses. Then it spread south along the river into Alaska.

# Alaska's Weed Warrior

**Lori Zaumseil** thinks white sweetclover is pretty. "It looks like a big, tall tumbleweed with pretty white flowers," she says. "But it doesn't play nice. Once you get it started, you can't stop it."

Lori started CANWIN, which stands for Citizens Against Noxious Weeds Invading the North.

"We're not talking about your father's dandelion that's just a nuisance and destroys how you want your grass to look," Lori says. A weed like white sweetclover "truly, truly changes the environment."

To get the word out, Lori talks and writes to everyone she can.

"I have the gift of gab and the ability to write a pretty mean letter," she says.

Lori convinced her state to fight the weeds. "If you arm yourself with knowledge and information, you will get people to help you," she says. "You will get people to listen."

## Pulling Up White Sweetclover

As fourth-graders, Girl Scouts **Cathryn Papasodora** (pictured at right) and **Mykela Carroll** pulled white sweetclover from Alaska's Chugach National Forest. Nearly 100 Girl Scouts and Forest Service scientists worked to pull up the clover, too.

The girls also pulled out alsike clover and pineapple weed. Then they planted sedge seeds. Sedge is a flowering plant that's good for the area. "It's important to do this because you're helping the environment," Mykela says.

# SEEDS, NUTS, FRUITS, AND CONES

Seeds and nuts come in all shapes and sizes. Sometimes they have shells around them, or fruit, or cones. Can you find the apple, sunflower, and orange seeds below? How about the dandelion seeds? And the pine nuts and chestnuts?

# The Delights of Dirt Candy

**Amanda Cohen** thinks fresh fruits and vegetables are as sweet as candy. She calls them "dirt candy."

Dirt Candy is the name of Amanda's New York restaurant, too.

Amanda likes to cook with seeds and nuts—even sunflower seeds and pine nuts.

"I was never a picky eater," says Amanda. "I was always willing to try everything."

When Amanda makes a salad, she tops it with candied grapefruit pops. She takes juicy pieces of grapefruit and dips them in a sweet coating. Then she puts them on a stick.

She also puts teeny-tiny grilled-cheese sandwiches in her salad.

Amanda's candied fruit pops might be a nice way to celebrate this journey. Ask an adult to help you make some! Dip them in whipped cream, in honor of Dairyland! If you like nuts, dip them in a sweet nut cream made from nuts and apple juice.

Amanda says oranges, bananas, strawberries, and star fruit are also good choices for fruit pops.

**AMANDA TOPS HER SALADS WITH SWEET FRUIT POPS.**

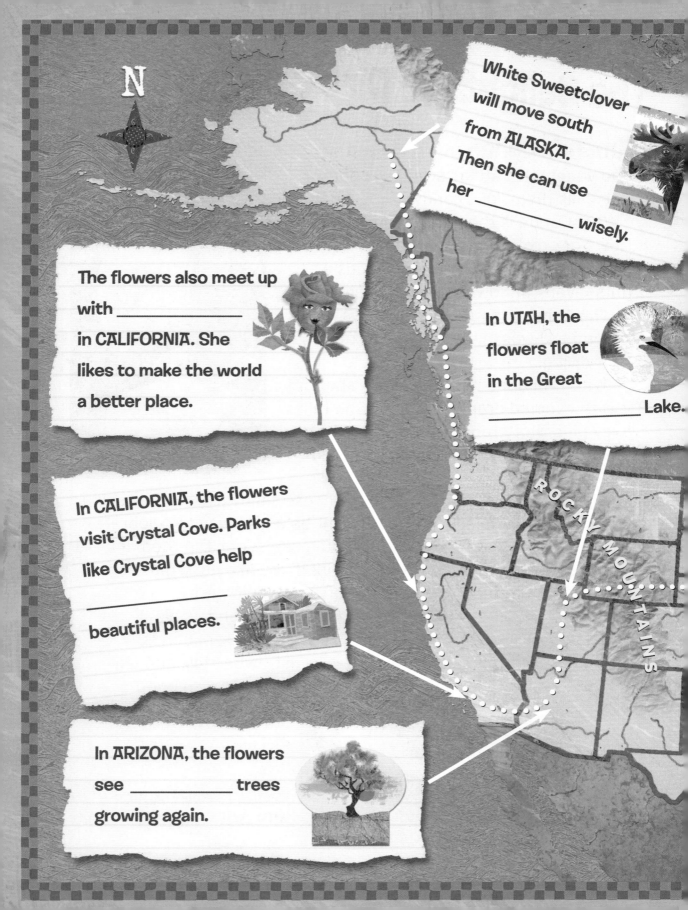

White Sweetclover will move south from ALASKA. Then she can use her _____ wisely.

The flowers also meet up with _____ in CALIFORNIA. She likes to make the world a better place.

In UTAH, the flowers float in the Great _____ Lake.

In CALIFORNIA, the flowers visit Crystal Cove. Parks like Crystal Cove help _____ beautiful places.

In ARIZONA, the flowers see _____ trees growing again.

N

ROCKY MOUNTAINS

# Road Trip Memories

## Sunshine, Fresh Air, New Places to See, The Best Travels Have All Three of These!

In WISCONSIN's Dairyland, the flowers eat lots of _____. They also make a new _____ named Jaz.

In MAINE, the flowers eat wild _____. Eating foods that grow near you is good for you and _____.

In PITTSBURGH, Sunny cleans soil so gardens can grow. She's being _____. That's living the Girl Scout Law!

| | 0 | 500 | 1,000 |
|---|---|---|---|
| Miles | | | |
| Kilometers | | | |
| | 0 | 500 | 1,000 | 1,500 |

# My Journey Never Ends!

Like fireflies Lucy and Ace, I will use a special skill to help my friends.
My special skill is

_____

I earned my Blue Bucket Award by teaching others that

_____

Like Clover, I plan to use resources wisely wherever I go! I'll start by

_____

## Here are my favorite seeds, leaves, and petals!

I will always remember: Nice souvenirs might be leaves and
petals that fall to the ground—but not living things!